Assault on Yavin Four

#1
ASSAULT ON YAVIN FOUR

RYDER WINDHAM

SCHOLASTIC INC.
New York Toronto London Auckland Sydney

ISBN 0-590-12793-4

12 11 10 9 8 7 6 5 4   7 8 9/9 0 1 2/0

Printed in the U.S.A.   40

First Scholastic printing, September 1997

INTRODUCTION

For many years, the evil Empire tried to control the galaxy. The Empire was battled by the Rebel Alliance. The Rebels hoped to bring an end to the Emperor's rule.

The Empire's most fearsome weapon was the Death Star, a giant space station that could destroy entire planets. The Death Star was created by an Imperial officer named Grand Moff Tarkin.

When Grand Moff Tarkin learned that the Rebels were hiding on a moon called Yavin Four, Tarkin tried to use the Death Star to destroy the entire moon.

In an incredible battle, a young Rebel pilot named Luke Skywalker fired two proton torpedoes from his X-wing starfighter. The torpedoes caused the entire Death Star to explode. Yavin Four was saved.

One of the few survivors of the Death Star was Darth Vader. After the Death Star exploded, Vader's TIE fighter went spinning into deep space. For a short while afterward, Vader did not reach an Imperial station, and the Empire did not yet know that the Death Star had been destroyed.

The day after the great battle, Luke Skywalker, Princess Leia, Han Solo, Chewbacca the Wookiee, and the droids See-Threepio and Artoo-Detoo were still celebrating their victory on Yavin Four.

On the other side of the galaxy, an Imperial warship waited for a secret message from Grand Moff Tarkin. Its crew did not know that Tarkin perished on the Death Star . . .

PRELIMINARY MISSION

CHAPTER ONE

On the far side of the galaxy, an Imperial Star Destroyer hovered near the multiringed planet Delrakkin. The Star Destroyer was a gigantic wedge-shaped ship, carrying thousands of stormtroopers and six squadrons of TIE fighters.

Admiral Termo entered the bridge of the Star Destroyer, and the stormtroopers stepped out of his way. Termo walked over to Communications Officer Tix. In a low voice — almost a whisper — Admiral Termo asked, "Where is the report from the Death Star?"

Officer Tix nervously turned to meet Termo's gaze. No one liked to look into Termo's eyes. Tix tried not to sound scared as he replied, "We have not yet received any message from the Yavin system, Admiral."

"You confirmed the frequency of the hyperspace transponder?" asked Termo. The hyperspace transponder allowed messages to be sent at faster-than-lightspeed.

"Yes, sir. There's nothing wrong with our computers," Officer Tix answered. "If you wish to contact the Death Star, I am prepared to send a message . . . "

"If I *wanted* to send a message, I would have *told* you to send a message," said Termo. His voice remained calm, but Tix knew the admiral was angry. Admiral Termo hated officers who said anything unless he asked them a question.

Tix kept his hands on his keyboard and tried to keep his fingers from shaking. He was very scared.

"Our orders were *most* clear," Termo continued. "We

are to wait at Delrakkin until we receive the signal. Is that understood?"

"Yes, Admiral," rasped Tix.

Termo turned his gaze to the starboard viewport, and Tix exhaled a thin sigh of relief. Beyond the viewport, the green planet Delrakkin rotated slowly on its axis. Termo noticed a dark, cloudy spiral that churned on the planet's western hemisphere. He watched the spiral for several seconds. "Would a planetary storm cause any disruption for the transmission?" he asked.

"No, sir," Tix responded. "Not at this range."

"This is most unusual," said Termo thoughtfully. Tix thought Admiral Termo sounded unsure of himself. Tix was so surprised by this that he almost didn't hear what Termo whispered next.

"Something must have happened to Grand Moff Tarkin."

Admiral Termo turned to a brightly lit console and spoke into a comm unit. "Admiral Termo to Captain Skeezer. Report to forward launch bay, and prepare the long-range assault shuttle for immediate departure to the Yavin system."

On the moon Yavin Four, the celebration was still going strong. The Death Star had been destroyed, and the Rebels were joyous in their victory over the Empire.

The Rebels had transformed the ruins of an ancient temple into a hangar for the Rebel fleet. But the hangar was eerily empty. Most of the Rebels' ships had been destroyed the day before, during their battle with the Death Star.

"Hey, kid," said Han Solo as he entered the hangar. "We've been looking everywhere for you!"

Luke Skywalker stood beside his X-wing starfighter. He had been working on his proton-torpedo launcher. He glanced up to see Solo and Chewbacca the Wookiee walk toward him.

"Hi, Han," said Luke. "Hey there, Chewie."

"What're you doing here?" asked Solo. "Why aren't you at the victory party with the rest of us Rebels?"

"I'm making some special changes to my X-wing's weapons system," Luke replied.

"Oh, like *you* need help firing a proton torpedo?" said Solo with a grin. Just the day before, Luke had fired the incredible shots that destroyed the Death Star. Chewbacca growled and gave Luke Skywalker a friendly pat on the back. Luke smiled.

"Sure, Chewie, give all the credit to him," joked Solo. He turned to Luke. "Kid, if I hadn't seen you make those shots, I would've said it couldn't be done." Han shook his head. "I mean, take it from a guy who's toasted a few womp rats himself. You did *real* good up there."

"Thanks, Han," Luke said. "I really can't believe it, either. I just hope I never have to do something like that again!"

"Something like what?" asked Princess Leia Organa as she entered the hangar.

"Haven't you heard?" asked Solo, wrapping an arm around Luke's shoulder. "We're the guys who destroyed the Death Star."

"Oh, you're still bragging about *that*?" joked the princess. "How does it feel, Solo, being a hero for a change?"

"It's not so different . . . from the usual me," Han replied with a mild shrug. "But on the other hand," he smiled, "I kind of like the effect it has on princesses."

"Sure," said Leia. "It makes us all want to run away."

Chewbacca let loose with a loud roar that alarmed everyone but Han, who knew that the Wookiee was laughing at him.

"Laugh it up, furball," said Solo. "Just remember who pays you."

Leia turned her attention to Luke. "Trouble with your X-wing, Master Skywalker?"

"Huh?" Luke said, feeling himself blush at the princess's pretend formality. "No, I was, um, just making a few adjustments to the armaments. It was Wedge's idea." Wedge Antilles was another Rebel pilot, and a friend of Luke's.

"It's wise to be prepared," Leia said. "We lost too many brave pilots in this last battle. I don't want to lose any more."

A mournful silence fell across the group as they remembered the Rebel Alliance's losses. But soon the sound of metal footsteps approached from the darkness. In moments, a gleaming, golden figure emerged.

"Thank goodness I've found you!" said See-Threepio. He waved his arms grandly in a gesture to Luke and the others. "These ruins are so vast, it's a wonder that anyone can find anything at all!"

"What's wrong now?" Solo groaned. "Did you lose your little pal?"

"What? Who?" asked Threepio. Threepio prided himself in his fluency in over six million languages. But he sometimes had great difficulty understanding Han Solo. "Oh! You mean Artoo-Detoo?"

"No, I meant the technician that got you perfectly polished in time for the victory ceremony."

"Oh, no, I'm not looking for *her*," said Threepio. "But she *did* do an *excellent* job, didn't she?"

"Han is joking with you, Threepio," said Luke. "Are you looking for Artoo?"

"Artoo? No, I know where *he* is. Oh, you've got my circuits all confused! I was looking for all of you. Artoo is in the briefing room, and he's discovered something that may be of great importance!"

"Then we better get to the briefing room," said Leia, already on her way with Luke beside her. Solo began to move with them, but Threepio stepped before him.

"Excuse me, Master Solo," he said, "but I wonder whether you could explain to me why you . . . *joke* with me?"

"Sure, I'll explain it," said Solo, aiming an index finger at Threepio's sternum. As Threepio lowered his chin to see Solo's finger on his chestplate, Solo brought his finger up fast so that it rapped against Threepio's olfactory sensor. Threepio jerked his head back in surprise.

Solo grinned. "It's because I like you."

"You like me?" said Threepio. "Really? How very generous of you, Captain Solo!"

Chewbacca growled at Solo. The Wookiee thought Solo was being mean, teasing Threepio like that. Chewbacca stepped forward and wiped away the smudge that Solo's finger had caused. Then he and Solo left the hangar.

"Oh!" said Threepio. "I guess that means you like me too, Chewbacca. How wonderful! . . . Oh, dear! Wait for me!"

CHAPTER TWO

Captain Skeezer stood at attention in the forward launch bay of the Imperial Star Destroyer. Behind him, four crewmen, three stormtrooper squads, and three Imperial pilots prepared to board the downsized Carrack light cruiser. At nearly half the length of the typical Carrack, Skeezer's modified vessel carried only three external TIE fighters. Still, it boasted a powerful hyperdrive engine.

Admiral Termo strode into the launch bay and crossed directly to Skeezer. As always, Termo's voice remained low and calm.

"We have lost contact with Grand Moff Tarkin," said Termo. "Go to the Yavin system and investigate, but do not attempt to contact the Death Star. Is that clear?"

"Yes, sir," said Skeezer. His face was completely blank. Skeezer never showed emotion.

"Do not attempt to transmit any hyperspace comm from Yavin," added Termo. "It is possible that the transmissions are being intercepted by the Rebellion. You will return here when you have determined the status of the Death Star . . . and have dealt with it."

"Yes, sir," said Skeezer.

Admiral Termo turned on his heel and walked out of the launch bay. It wasn't until the sliding doors had sealed behind the departed admiral that the chief gunnery officer approached Captain Skeezer.

"May I ask the nature of our mission, Captain Skeezer?" the gunnery officer asked. He noticed that Captain Skeezer looked concerned. Captain Skeezer *never* looked concerned.

"Lieutenant," said Skeezer, "our mission is to find out whether we are in a whole world of trouble."

The hologram of the Death Star was suspended in the front of the briefing room. Artoo was jacked into the holoprojector's computer, and he adjusted the rotation of the three-dimensional image. Artoo removed the exterior hull, revealing the Death Star's interior design.

"I know the Death Star is gone," said Leia, "but the sight of its hologram makes my blood run cold."

"Relax, Princess," said Solo. "That thing ain't *ever* coming back."

Luke kept his eyes on the hologram. "Why did Artoo dredge up the Death Star plans?" he asked Threepio.

"Oh, you know Artoo," Threepio replied. "He can't leave anything alone until he's looked at it from every angle. I thought his experience in the Death Star battle would have cured him of his curiosity. But it didn't. After his repairs were made, he couldn't wait to have another look at the plans."

Solo rolled his eyes. "Why're we wasting our time, looking at the floor plans of a place that doesn't even exist anymore?"

"Well," said Threepio, "when we were onboard the Death Star, Artoo plugged into its computer network to locate Princess Leia. While searching the network, Artoo noted the Death Star was carrying an *extremely* large amount of *bacta*."

Everyone knew about the chemical compound called bacta. Bacta was regarded as a miracle of modern science. Bacta could heal almost any wound. Injured people could be put into bacta tanks and the bacta would make them better almost immediately.

"What a waste," said Solo. "You wouldn't believe how much people along the Outer Rim will pay for bacta!"

Leia shot Solo an icy glance. "Don't you ever stop thinking about money? That bacta could have saved a lot of lives!"

"Yeah, well there's no use arguing about it, your worshipfulness," said Solo, "because it's gone!"

"Wait a minute," said Luke. "Bacta is used to heal people. Why would the Death Star be carrying so much?"

Artoo-Detoo let out a flurry of beeps and whistles.

"That's precisely what Artoo-Detoo was wondering!" exclaimed Threepio. "According to the plans, the Death Star's medical stations were equipped with their own sufficient supply of bacta. It would seem that this extra bacta was *cargo*."

"Maybe they were expecting heavy casualties somewhere," said Solo. "And if there's one thing I *don't* care about, it's dead Imperials."

Leia ignored Solo's bravado. "It just doesn't make sense," she said. "The Imperial Navy isn't even sympathetic to *their own* wounded."

"And once the Empire built the Death Star," added Luke, "they probably didn't expect to lose *any* battles . . . "

"Oh, dear!" said Threepio suddenly, raising a hand to his head. "My broadband antenna has received a relay signal from our beacon satellite! A ship of unknown origin has entered the Yavin system!"

CHAPTER THREE

Although he did not know what awaited him in the Yavin system, Captain Skeezer thought he would be glad to be out of hyperspace. The mere thought of the faster-than-light travel gave Skeezer a headache. But he felt even more uncomfortable as the Carrack's sensors searched for the Death Star.

"Where is it?" asked the gunnery officer. "It's got to be . . . *somewhere*."

Skeezer squinted at Yavin, the giant gas planet. His headache was not getting any better. "Which of Yavin's moons can support human life?" he barked to the gunnery officer.

"Yavin Four, Eight, and Thirteen," responded the gunnery officer.

"Four's closest," said Skeezer. "We'd better take a look."

"I'm sorry to have to say this," said General Dodonna, "but our victory celebration has come to an end." General Dodonna was the Alliance officer who planned the attack on the Death Star.

Luke, Leia, Solo, Chewbacca, and the droids were assembled in the war room. Wedge Antilles and the other surviving starfighter pilots were also present.

"Thirty-five minutes ago," said Dodonna, "our satellite beacon picked up an unidentified vessel." On a large monitor behind Dodonna, a small white rectangle slowly appeared against a star field.

Dodonna pointed to the slowly moving rectangle. "Sensors indicated the vessel's length at one hundred fifty meters. Its entrance into our system indicates that it emerged from hyperspace. We hoped it might be an Alliance ship, but if you look at our computer's enhancement of the vessel, you'll see something very interesting."

The screen flickered, and the white rectangle became larger. It was still difficult to see. But several seconds later, the white rectangle passed in front of the brightly illuminated Yavin, becoming a more distinct silhouette.

"That vessel's carrying TIE fighters!" exclaimed Luke.

"Three, to be exact," Dodonna confirmed. "Because they're mounted on the exterior of the ship, we think the vessel is a modified Carrack assault cruiser. Besides the TIE fighters, it probably carries landspeeders and laser cannons. It might have been expecting to meet the Death Star."

"Or," offered Leia, "the Empire sent it here to find out why they haven't heard from Grand Moff Tarkin."

"Either way," said General Dodonna, "it confirms that our battle with the Empire is far from over. But rather than fight this one out, our best strategy is to wait and hope for the cruiser to pass by. Then we can continue our —"

"Hope for it to pass?" Luke yelled. He startled everyone, including himself, with his outburst. "But General . . . There are enough of us! We can take out that cruiser right now!"

Leia put her hand on Luke's arm. "Please, Luke," she said. "You're our best pilot, and one of the few we have left. We can't afford to lose you!"

"I . . . I guess you're right," Luke agreed.

"Well, folks, this is great fun," said an annoyed Solo, "but instead of waiting around here, I should do some spring cleaning on the *Falcon*. Come on, Chewie." The Wookiee and Solo left the briefing room.

General Dodonna addressed the remaining audience. "We will continue to monitor the vessel with our sensors, and will keep you posted of any developments. This concludes our meeting." Dodonna stepped away from his podium, and the large monitor screen went blank.

Luke turned to Wedge Antilles. "I can't believe they're making us sit this one out, Wedge!"

"Believe it, Luke," Wedge replied. "It's lousy, but the general's right. We can't risk losing any pilots right now, especially in a minor skirmish."

Suddenly, from the direction of the hangar, the sound of a distant, familiar roar reached the meeting room.

"Hey!" said Luke. "Those are the *Falcon*'s engines!"

Leia thought of the reckless Han Solo. "Oh, no!" she cried, her eyes wide with fear. "He wouldn't disobey orders . . . would he?"

The *Millennium Falcon* rocketed out of the makeshift hangar and rose swiftly above the green trees that surrounded the Rebel base. From his copilot seat, Chewbacca uttered a whimpering howl.

"Oh, stop your whining," said Solo. "You could've stayed."

Chewbacca howled again.

"No, I'm not trying to impress the princess!" snapped Solo. "I just don't like waiting around for a fight!"

The *Falcon* blew through the atmosphere and stars filled the view from the cockpit. Han adjusted the navi-computer, then climbed out of his seat. "Okay, Chewie, stay on target! We've got to hit 'em fast and hard!" Solo ran to the aft laser cannon.

Within seconds, the Carrack cruiser came into view. The *Falcon* descended upon it from a dangerously close angle. The Carrack tilted slightly, indicating the Imperial pilot's delayed response. Glowing bolts sprayed from the ship's laser cannons toward the *Falcon*. Only it was too late.

As the *Falcon* soared past the vessel, Solo squeezed off a shot and took out the Carrack's sensor array. Then he fired four more blasts at the externally mounted TIE fighters. Explosions tore at the hull of the Carrack.

"Waaaah-hoo!" yelled Solo over the comm to Chewbacca. "Chain reaction!"

The *Falcon* circled back for another attack, but the damaged Carrack fired its thrusters and hurtled through space in the direction of Yavin Four. Chewbacca stayed on the Carrack's tail as both ships entered Yavin Four's atmosphere. Solo continued to fire upon the Imperial ship.

"Stang!" Solo exclaimed. "They've put most of their power into their rear deflector shields! Don't let 'em out of your sight, Chewie!"

Three blasts fired from the fleeing Carrack's cannons. A second later, they struck the cockpit of the *Millennium Falcon*. The *Falcon*'s shields absorbed most of the impact, but Chewbacca howled to Solo as smoke filled the cockpit interior.

"Chewie!" Solo yelled into his comm, "You okay?!"

Chewbacca growled in the affirmative.

"We've got no choice, Chewie!" said Solo. "Set us down near the Rebel base!" Solo took a last look at the Carrack, just in time to see it land near a towering ruin. Solo left his position and ran for the cockpit.

Solo and Chewbacca landed the *Falcon* outside the Rebel base. The exterior of the *Falcon*'s cockpit was badly scorched. As Solo and Chewbacca exited their ship, Luke and Leia ran to them from the hangar. General Dodonna followed.

"What were you trying to do up there?!" yelled Leia. "Get yourself killed?!"

"Who, me?" said Solo, trying to look innocent. "I was only trying to help —"

"You disobeyed an order from General Dodonna, Captain Solo!" Leia was furious. "If you're going to be a soldier, you have to play by our rules!"

Chewbacca growled at Solo.

"What're you blaming *me* for?!" Solo asked the giant Wookiee. "*You* know I'm no good at following orders!"

Chewbacca snorted.

"All right, so I'll try harder," Solo agreed. Then Han caught Luke's gaze. Luke looked more angry than Solo could have imagined. Solo realized that he had disappointed Luke. All of a sudden, he felt ashamed.

"You're right, Princess," Solo admitted. "I shouldn't have taken off like that." He turned to General Dodonna. "I'm sorry, sir."

"We'll talk later, Solo," said Dodonna. "What happened to the cruiser?"

"We destroyed the sensor array and the three TIE fighters before they made a run for it. It looked like they crash-landed about eight kilometers from here, near some other ruins."

"If there are any survivors," said Dodonna, "we have to stop them from sending a distress signal to the Empire."

"We'll have to find the ship's captain, too," Leia added. "He may be the only one who can tell us the purpose of their mission here."

"Then we'd better get moving," scowled Luke, "if we're going to finish what Han started!"

The Rebels ran for the hangar. There wasn't a moment to lose.

MISSION BRIEFING

Before you proceed, you must consult the Mission Guide for the rules of the STAR WARS MISSIONS. You must follow these rules at all times.

This is a Rebel mission.

The Imperial ship crashed eight kilometers east of the Rebel base on Yavin Four. If any Imperial stormtroopers survived the crash of their ship, they will attempt to contact the Empire. If a message reaches the Empire, more Imperial forces will be sent to Yavin Four. The Rebel base would not survive an attack so soon after the Death Star battle.

There are many ancient towers and pyramids on Yavin Four, and the stormtroopers may try to hide in these ruins. They might also prepare an attack on the Rebel base.

You have to act fast. You do not want more stormtroopers to come to Yavin Four, and you do not want any of your friends to be attacked by stormtroopers.

Your goal is to prevent the stormtroopers from launching an emergency distress beacon and from attacking the Rebel base on Yavin Four. You must also attempt to capture the Imperial captain of the crashed ship.

You start this mission with one thousand Mission Points (1,000 MP).

Choose your character. You can take no more than four weapons (including a blaster rifle and a blaster pistol) and three vehicles (including a speeder bike). You can use your Powers twice in this Mission.

May the Force be with you.

Your Mission: Attack on Yavin Four

There isn't enough time for General Dodonna to give anyone a full briefing, but the orders are clear. Search and destroy. Rebels are running all over the hangar deck, grabbing their gear and preparing for the mission. You try to remain calm, but it isn't easy.

General Dodonna pulls you aside. "Do you think you can lead the mission to the crash site, and scout for any signs of stormtrooper activity?" he asks.

"I'll do my best, General," you reply.

Dodonna nods. "The Rebellion is counting on you."

You are issued a speeder bike to travel the eight kilometers to the ruins. The speeder bike is equipped with a navicomputer, so you'll know whether you are traveling in the right direction. The jungles are dense on Yavin Four, and it's easy to get lost.

You are also issued a small comlink that straps to your shoulder; you will use this unit to communicate with General Dodonna.

As an added precaution, you are given a pair of infrared goggles. These goggles will allow you to see in the dark. The jungle is thick with shadows, and you might not be able to see without infrared vision.

Finally, you are issued a blaster pistol and a blaster rifle. You may already have your own weapon, but you need these two extra ones just in case. You are familiar with both the pistol and the rifle, and you are not afraid to use them. You put both weapons in a compartment on your speeder bike.

As you climb onto the bike, you look back at your friends. They know you have been chosen to lead the way to the Imperial crash site. Some of your friends look worried. After all, they might never see you again. You try not to think about it, and instead concentrate on getting your job done. You hit the throttle and the bike rockets out of the hangar and into the dense jungle forest of Yavin Four.

The navicomputer confirms that you're going in the right direction. You fly between the trees at high speed. You can't afford to waste any time.

The trees are so tall and their branches are so thick that they have cast the jungle floor into a great darkness. You are barely one kilometer away from the Rebel base when you have to slow to a stop. Out of reflex, you almost turn on the bike's headlight. Then it occurs to you: bad idea! If you turn on your headlight, the Imperials will see you approach.

Fortunately, you have your infrared goggles. You pull them over your eyes and touch a button on the side. The jungle suddenly becomes clearly visible.

You speak into the comlink that's strapped to your shoulder. "General Dodonna?" you say. "Warn the others that it's really dark out here. Unless everyone wears infrared goggles, they might not be able to make it through this jungle!"

You rev the engine and take off.

Five kilometers later, you reach a clearing in the jungle. You've discovered another set of ruins. Little is known about the ancient builders of the fortresses on this moon. No one knew how they were able to cut and transport huge stone blocks from the crust of Yavin Four, or how those blocks were transformed into huge towers.

In the clearing you've discovered, trees can't grow because of the large rocky walls and foundations that spread out around the area. There are old stone stairways, pillars, and some high walls. With all the rocks lying around, it looks like the roof must have caved in a long, long time ago. You have another two kilometers to travel before you reach the Imperial cruiser. These are not the ruins you have to worry about, but you call back to the base.

"General Dodonna? I've arrived at some ruins. No sign of any Imperial activity yet."

"Keep moving," Dodonna insists. "And stay on your guard!"

You are about to speed away when you see a flash of light on the far side of the ruins. Perhaps it's the sunlight, reflecting off a piece of glass or metal.

Or maybe it's something else . . .

Without any warning, a branch swings in front of you and hits you in the chest. You are knocked off your bike, onto the ground.

Two stormtroopers emerge from behind some nearby trees. The first one carries the branch that hit you. The second one has a blaster rifle aimed at your head. You realize that they must be scouts from the crashed Imperial ship.

The first stormtrooper tosses the branch aside and steps over to you. You are still lying on the ground. He unholsters his rifle and aims it. He takes away your standard weapon, and tells you to take off your goggles. You take off your goggles and he gets a good look at your face. You hope he doesn't recognize you.

"Are you a member of the Rebel Alliance?!" demands the stormtrooper.

"No," you reply. "I'm a history student from the Academy. I'm studying the ancient ruins of Yavin Four so I can get a good grade in alien history."

"Prove it!" the stormtrooper orders.

"I have some research papers in a compartment on my speeder bike," you say. "I can show them to you."

The stormtroopers let you step over to your bike. They keep their guns leveled.

You open the compartment that contains the blaster pistol and the blaster rifle. The stormtroopers are standing behind you, and they can't see these weapons.

The blaster pistol is easier to pick up, but you will have to take aim and fire twice (once for each stormtrooper); the blaster rifle is heavier, but one pull on the trigger will spray laser bolts at both stormtroopers.

These two stormtroopers must be neutralized. You have to move very fast.

Choose one weapon, either the blaster pistol or the blaster rifle. (If you have questions about how to fight this confront, please consult page 20 of your Mission Guide.)

For the blaster pistol: Add your weaponry# to your weapon's mid-range# for your confront#. Roll the 6-dice to combat the first stormtrooper.

If your confront# is equal to or more than your roll#, add the difference to your Mission Points (MP) total and proceed to combat the second stormtrooper, using the same confront equation.

If your confront# is lower than your roll#, subtract the difference from your MP total and repeat this confront. Once you have defeated the first stormtrooper, repeat this confront for the second stormtrooper, using the same confront equation. Once you have defeated the second stormtrooper, you may proceed.

For the blaster rifle: Add your weaponry# to your weapon's mid-range# +1 for your confront#. Roll the 12-dice to combat both stormtroopers.

If your confront# is equal to or more than your roll#, add the difference to your MP total and proceed.

If your confront# is lower than your roll#, subtract the difference from your MP total. Now double your confront# for your new confront#. Roll the 12-dice again to continue to battle the stormtroopers.

If your new confront# is equal to or more than your roll#, you may proceed.

If your new confront# is lower than your roll#, subtract the difference from your MP total. Repeat this confront with the same new confront# until you have defeated the stormtroopers. Then you may proceed.

Both stormtroopers have now been neutralized. You feel foolish for not having been more cautious. Did you really think that the stormtroopers were going to sit around their crashed ship? You were lucky this time. You'll have to be more careful.

You are almost afraid to tell General Dodonna what happened. After all, he asked *you* to be the scout, and you practically walked into the hands of stormtroopers. But it's your duty to tell him so he can warn the other Rebels. From now on, stormtroopers could be anywhere.

Unfortunately, your comlink is broken. Something must have happened to it when you were knocked off your speeder bike.

You drag the stormtroopers to a stone wall and lay them over the top. This way, anyone who comes by can see them. If the Rebels see the stormtroopers, your friends will know you are alive and doing a fine job. If other stormtroopers find their fallen comrades, they'll think twice before they attack you.

The sunlight reflects off the stormtroopers' armor. You remember the flash of light that distracted you earlier, just before you were knocked off your speeder bike. You wonder whether the light might have reflected off the armor of *another* stormtrooper.

After putting both the blaster pistol and the blaster rifle back in the bike's storage compartment you climb onto your bike, and speed to the area where you saw the flash of light.

You park your speeder bike beside some rocks and walk quietly forward. Pushing aside some branches, you see three stormtroopers. They do not see you.

The stormtroopers are busy assembling a small rocket launcher. Now you know why they came to this clearing.

The dense jungle trees must have gotten in the way of a rocket launch. They needed an open space to launch their distress beacon.

The stormtroopers are standing near a landspeeder. You can try to neutralize the stormtroopers (one at a time or all at once). But if you miss one shot, a stormtrooper might escape in the landspeeder.

You want to deactivate the Imperial distress beacon. You do not want to shoot the beacon. If you do, you might be injured by the accidental explosion.

Note: You must defeat all three stormtroopers before you can deactivate the Imperial distress beacon. If you roll the 12-dice and your roll# equals your confront# minus 1, you have accidentally shot the Imperial distress beacon and caused it to explode. You suffer a minor injury, and must subtract 10MP from your MP total.

This can only happen once. If you accidentally shoot the beacon again, do not subtract another 10MP from your MP total.

To neutralize the stormtroopers: Choose your weapon. You can either try to neutralize the stormtroopers all at once or one at a time.

All at once: Add your weaponry# to your weapon's mid-range# for your confront#. Roll the 12-dice to combat the first two stormtroopers.

If your confront# is equal to or more than your roll#, add the difference to your MP total and proceed to the third stormtrooper (p. 31).

If your confront# is lower than your roll#, subtract the difference from your MP total. Now double your confront# for your new confront#. Roll the 12-dice again to continue to battle the stormtroopers.

If your new confront# is equal to or more than your roll#, you may proceed to the third stormtrooper (next page).

If your new confront# is lower than your roll#, subtract the difference from your MP total. Repeat this confront with your new confront# until you have defeated the two stormtroopers. Then *proceed to the third stormtrooper* (next page).

One at a time: Add your weaponry# to your weapon's far-range# for your confront#. Roll the 12-dice to combat the first stormtrooper.

If your confront# is equal to or more than your roll#, you may proceed to combat the second stormtrooper, using the same confront equation.

If your confront# is lower than your roll#, subtract the difference from your MP total and repeat this confront, adding +3 to your confront# for your new confront#. Once you have defeated the first stormtrooper, *repeat this confront* for the second stormtrooper, using your new confront#.

Once you have defeated the second stormtrooper, you may proceed to confront the third stormtrooper (next page).

The third stormtrooper: At this stage, you only have one chance to defeat the third stormtrooper. Add your weaponry# to your weapons mid-range# +2 for your confront#. Roll the 12-dice to combat the third stormtrooper.

If your confront# is equal to or more than your roll#, add 15 MP to your MP total and proceed to disarm the Imperial distress beacon.

If your confront# is lower than your roll#, the stormtrooper escapes to the landspeeder, and you must subtract the difference from your MP total. You must *pursue the landspeeder.*

To pursue the landspeeder: You may either choose to jump onto the landspeeder and fight the stormtrooper at close range with your bare hands, or you may leap onto your speeder bike and pursue the stormtrooper at long range with the speeder's weapon.

At close range: Add your strength# and your skill# to your weapon's close-range# for your confront#. Roll the 12-dice to combat the stormtrooper.

If your confront# is equal to or more than your roll#, you may add the difference to your MP total and proceed to disarm the Imperial distress beacon.

If your confront# is lower than your roll#, subtract the difference from your MP total. Add +2 to your old confront# for your new confront#. Repeat this confront with the same new confront# until you have defeated the stormtrooper. When you have defeated the stormtrooper, you may proceed to deactivate the Imperial distress beacon.

At long range: Add your weaponry# to your speeder bike's weaponry# for your confront#. Roll the 6-dice to combat the stormtrooper.

If your confront# is equal to or more than your roll#, add the difference to your MP total and proceed to deactivate the Imperial distress beacon.

If your confront# is lower than your roll#, subtract the difference from your MP total and repeat this confront until you have defeated the stormtrooper. When you have defeated the stormtrooper, you may proceed to deactivate the Imperial distress beacon.

You approach the beacon, and notice a small screen with blinking numbers on it . . . 10, 9, 8 . . . The troopers have activated a countdown mechanism, and the beacon will launch in a few seconds! Luckily, you have the training to deactivate it. You have to concentrate — and work fast!

To deactivate the Imperial distress beacon: Your skill# +1 is your confront#. Roll the 6-dice to deactivate the beacon.

If your confront# is equal to or more than your roll#, add the difference to your MP total and proceed.

If your confront# is lower than your roll#, subtract the difference from your MP total and repeat this confront until you have deactivated the beacon.

That was close! After you successfully deactivate the beacon, add 20MP to your total for a job well done. **Note:** If you accidentally shot the beacon before you defeated the stormtroopers, add 10MP to your total. If you are playing on the Advanced Level, add 50MP to your total.

The stormtroopers are now defeated and the beacon is no longer a problem. But your mission isn't over. There are more troopers out there, and their captain must be captured and brought in for questioning.

One of the neutralized stormtroopers wears an extra comlink on his belt. You remove the comlink and hold it up to your ear. You listen for signals from other stormtroopers, but do not hear any. That doesn't mean that you are safe; other stormtroopers may still be in the jungle.

You adjust the frequency setting on the comlink, and use a special code that will let General Dodonna know it's safe to broadcast. "General Dodonna?" you say. "I ran into trouble. I encountered five stormtroopers and had to neutralize them. But I was able to destroy the Imperial distress beacon!"

"Good work!" General Dodonna replies.

"Tell the others that there might be more stormtroopers in the jungle," you advise. "I'm moving on to the crash site."

You go to your speeder bike. You check your gear and ammunition. Your mind is racing. What will happen if you run into more stormtroopers? It was difficult to disable five stormtroopers. Are you prepared to disable twenty more?

If there are more stormtroopers, they will expect an attack from outside forces. At their crash site, they will have set up a strong defense to prevent anyone from reaching their ship. It would be almost impossible to attack their defense and survive.

But if you could sneak *inside* the crash site, you could combat the enemy where they least expect you. They are paying attention to the areas *around* the crash site, not *inside*. There's just one problem: How will you get inside?

You look at the defeated stormtroopers, then at their nearby landspeeder. You have an idea. It's a dangerous idea, but it just might work.

First, you attach your speeder bike to the landspeeder. You clamp it tightly to the back of the landspeeder so that it is secure. If you survive, you may need the speeder bike later.

You drag a stormtrooper over to the landspeeder and put him in the backseat.

You take another stormtrooper's armor and put it over your own clothes. You remove his helmet and place it over your head. It's not easy to see out of the helmet. *No wonder stormtroopers are such rotten shots!* you think. At least the stormtrooper's helmet has built-in infrared lenses so you'll be able to see in the dark.

Climbing into the Imperial landspeeder, you check the controls. The landspeeder has a navicomputer, so you can find the crash site. You turn on the engine and zoom away, towing your speeder bike with you.

Almost two kilometers later — very close to the crash site — you stop the landspeeder and climb out. You take your speeder bike off the back of the landspeeder and hide it under a very big tree. If you have to escape, your speeder bike will help you make a quick getaway.

You get back into the landspeeder, start the engine, and proceed through the jungle. Soon, you see the still-smoking wreckage of the Imperial Carrack cruiser. It has crashed into some trees and sits at an odd angle. The trees and the ship are at the base of an ancient tower.

You slow the landspeeder to a stop. Suddenly, you are surrounded by many stormtroopers. You have difficulty seeing behind you, but guess that there may be about twenty troopers.

Your fingers tighten on the steering wheel at the sight of the Imperial captain. You didn't think you'd encounter him so soon. The captain steps forward. His face looks like it is made of stone.

"Why have you returned without the others?!" he demands.

"We were attacked by a Rebel assault force, sir!" you reply. "The trooper in the backseat and I were the only two to survive! We raced back to warn you! We must prepare for a Rebel attack!"

The captain looks at the stormtrooper in the backseat. "I don't think," he observes, "that your comrade survived after all. Were you able to launch the distress beacon before you were attacked?"

"Yes, sir," you say.

The captain smiles. He thinks that the beacon has been launched and that the Empire will send a rescue team. "Everyone to your positions!" he orders. "Prepare for the Rebel assault!"

Without warning, your Imperial comlink beeps and a voice echoes from it: "This is General Dodonna. You haven't checked in and we're beginning to worry . . ."

You forgot to switch off the frequency!

The captain's face goes red with anger and he realizes you're a Rebel. He draws his blaster, but before he can fire, you punch the accelerator and the landspeeder rockets forward.

The captain fires a shot and it hits one of the landspeeder's thrusters. You lose control, and crash the speeder into the base of the ruins. High, vine-covered walls surround you as you leap out of the speeder and race to what looks like an entrance.

There are four stormtroopers at the entrance to the ruins.

You can choose to evade (avoid) or fight.

If you choose to fight, you can choose all at once or one at a time.

Note: You are still dressed as an Imperial stormtrooper. Because these four stormtroopers were inside the ruins when you arrived, they did not hear the message from General Dodonna. They do not know that you are a Rebel. In fact, they think you're a stormtrooper.

To evade (without Power): Add your charm# to your stealth# +5 for your confront#. Roll the 12-dice to evade the four stormtroopers.

If your confront# is equal to or more than your roll#, add the difference to your MP total and proceed into the ruins.

If your confront# is lower than your roll#, subtract the difference from your MP total. Your disguise is now useless and you will have to fight the four stormtroopers (below).

To evade (using Power)*: Choose your Evasion Power. Add your stealth# and Jedi# to your Power's low-resistance# for your confront#. Roll the 6-dice to evade the stormtroopers.

If your confront# is equal to or more than your roll#, add the difference to your MP total and proceed.

If your confront# is lower than your roll#, subtract the difference from your MP total. Your disguise is now useless and you will have to fight the four stormtroopers (below).

*Note: This counts as one of two Power uses you are allowed in this Mission.

To fight (one at a time): Choose your weapon. Add your weaponry# to your weapon's mid-range# for your confront#. Roll the 6-dice to combat the first stormtrooper.

If your confront# is equal to or more than your roll#, add the difference to your MP total and repeat this confront to combat the next stormtrooper.

If your confront# is lower than your roll#, subtract the difference from your MP total and repeat this confront, adding +1 to your old confront# for your new confront#. Repeat this confront until you have neutralized all four stormtroopers.

To fight (all at once): Add your weaponry# to your weapon's mid-range accuracy# +1 for your confront#. Roll the 12-dice to combat the stormtroopers.

If your confront# is equal to or more than your roll#, add the difference to your MP total and proceed to the ruins.

If your confront# is lower than your roll#, subtract the difference from your MP total and repeat this confront.

You have either evaded the stormtroopers or defeated them. Good job! If you have evaded them, add 20MP to your MP total. If you have fought them, add 10MP to your MP total. If you are playing on an Advanced Level, add 50MP for evasion and 40MP for fighting. You may now proceed into the ruins.

The clomping footsteps of more stormtroopers follow behind you, so you move quickly into the ruins.

You run down a narrow flight of stairs and enter a dark chamber. At the end of the chamber, you see an old doorway, framed in metal. An ancient lock secures the door.

The stormtroopers are coming down the stairs behind you. The stairway is narrow, and they'll have to come down one at a time. You can choose to fight the stormtroopers or to open the door.

To open the door, you can kick the door open, shoot the lock off, use Power to open the lock, or hotwire the lock. Choose now, then proceed.

Note: If you choose to fight the stormtroopers, you will not know how many you'll have to fight until you begin the confront. You must decide BEFORE you proceed. You must choose NOW whether you are going to fight all of the stormtroopers or open the door.

To fight the stormtroopers: Choose your weapon. Add your weaponry# to your weapon's close-range# +1 for your confront#. There are a total of six stormtroopers. You must repeat this confront until you have defeated the sixth stormtrooper. *Each time you defeat a stormtrooper, raise your confront# by +1.* When you defeat all of the stormtroopers, you may proceed through the door, which has been shot open.

Roll the 12-dice to combat the first stormtrooper.

If your confront# is equal to or more than your roll#, add the difference to your MP total and proceed to combat the next stormtrooper, adding +1 to your confront#.

If your confront# is lower than your roll#, subtract the difference from your MP total and repeat this confront.

To kick the door open: Your strength# +2 is your confront#. Roll the 6-dice to kick the door open.

If your confront# is equal to or more than your roll#, add the difference to your MP total and proceed to pass through the doorway.

If your confront# is lower than your roll#, subtract the difference from your MP total and repeat this confront until you have kicked the door open.

To shoot the lock off: Your weaponry# added to your weapon's low-range# is your confront#. Roll the 6-dice to shoot the lock off.

If your confront# is equal to or more than your roll#, add the difference to your MP total and proceed to pass through the doorway.

If your confront# is lower than your roll#, subtract the difference from your MP total and repeat this confront, adding +1 to your confront# for your new confront#. Using that same confront#, repeat until you have shot the lock off.

To use Power to open the lock*: Choose your Object Movement Power. Add your strength# and Jedi# to your Power's low-resist# for your confront#. Roll the 6-dice to open the lock.

If your confront# is equal to or more than your roll#, add the difference to your MP total and proceed.

If your confront# is lower than your roll#, subtract the difference from your MP total. Repeat this confront, subtracting 1 from your confront# for your new confront#. (Note: Your new confront# cannot be lower than 2.)

*Note: This counts as one of the two Power uses you are allowed on this Mission.

To hotwire the lock: Your skill# +2 is your confront#. Roll the 6-dice to hotwire the lock.

If your confront# is equal to or more than your roll#, add the difference to your MP total and proceed to pass through the doorway.

If your confront# is lower than your roll#, subtract the difference from your MP total and repeat this confront, subtracting 1 from your new confront#. (**Note:** Your new confront# cannot be lower than 2.)

After the door is opened you may proceed inside the next chamber. It's been quite a run for you. Add 20MP to your MP total (40MP for Advanced Level players).

You slam the door behind you and spot a metal beam on the floor. You lift the beam and brace it against the door so that no one will be able to push the door open from the other side. It won't take a stormtrooper long to blow up the door, but the brace will buy you some time. You must find another way out of the ruins!

"General Dodonna?" you speak into your comlink. But it's no good. You can't send a transmission from the inside of this fortress.

You take off your stormtrooper helmet and strap it to your back. You adjust your infrared goggles so you can see in the darkness. When you step forward, something snaps beneath your feet. You look down.

Bones. Bones. And more bones.

The floor of the room is littered with the crumbling remains of skeletons. Some of the skeletons are human, and some are alien. All of the skeletons are broken and scattered, covered by a thick layer of dust. It seems that a furious battle took place here countless years ago.

You pick up part of an ancient shield. What could have caused such a deadly mess?

You search the room to see if there's another way out. There's a vent in the floor. It might be an airshaft.

There's another door at the far end of the room. It's an old door, and very heavy. You open it and reveal an ancient droid.

The droid is tall, lean, and covered with dust. It stands alone inside a large cabinet, with almost no space around it. The droid has three dark optical sensors for its eyes. Each of its three arms ends with a vibro-ax — a weapon that can slice through bones as if they were made of air! You wonder if the droid once guarded the room.

Suddenly, the droid's eyes blink red. It's operational! By opening the door, you have activated its defenses. It raises a vibro-ax menacingly and steps forward.

You fire a blast at the droid's head, but this has no effect on its armor plating. If you fight this droid, you will have to dislocate each of its deadly arms.

You can choose to evade or fight.

Note: If you choose to fight and you defeat the droid, you will gain one vibro-ax.

To evade (without Power): Your stealth# +2 is your confront#. Roll the 6-dice to leap down into the vent.

If your confront# is equal to or more than your roll#, add the difference to your MP total and proceed.

If your confront# is lower than your roll#, subtract the difference from your MP total and repeat this confront until you have successfully evaded the droid.

To evade (using Power)*: Choose your Evasion Power. Add your stealth# and Jedi# to your Power's mid-resist# for your confront#. Roll the 6-dice to evade the stormtroopers.

If your confront# is equal to or more than your roll#, add the difference to your MP total and proceed.

If your confront# is lower than your roll#, subtract the difference from your MP total and repeat this confront.

*Note: This counts as one of two Power uses you are allowed in this Mission.

To fight: Choose your weapon. Add your weaponry# to your weapon's mid-range# for your confront#. Roll the 6-dice to disable one of the droid's arms.

If your confront# is equal to or more than your roll#, add the difference to your MP total and proceed to disable the droid's second arm using the same confront equation.

If your confront# is lower than your roll#, subtract the difference from your MP total. Now double your confront# +1 for your new confront#. Roll the 12-dice to continue to combat the ancient droid.

Once you have disabled all three of the droid's arms, the droid falls to the floor. It has been drained of energy. You pick up one of its fallen vibro-axes. Now you may climb down into the vent. Add 10MP to your MP total (25MP for Advanced Level players).

Note: If you have disabled the ancient droid, you do not have to roll any dice to enter the vent.

You are in the vent, in an airshaft below the droid room. It's a low-ceilinged shaft and you have to crawl on your hands and knees. As you move forward, you wonder about the ancient civilization that built this place. You wonder about the purpose of this tower. Was the droid placed in the upper chamber to guard or protect something?

You are thinking about all of this when you hear a loud creaking sound. The shaft cannot support your weight. You try to back up, but it's too late. The floor of the shaft breaks open and you fall into the darkness below.

You land hard on a stone floor. You are lucky: You are still alive, and you have not broken any bones. But you are also deeper within the ancient tower — perhaps even farther from finding your way out.

A loud humming sound fills the air. A strange blue light illuminates the room. You turn off your infrared goggles.

There does not appear to be any way out of this chamber. There are no doors and no vents, except for the broken vent hanging high above your head.

There is a round stone table in the middle of the room. A large, glowing marble floats in the air above it. Wondering if the marble might activate a hidden door, you reach out and touch its surface.

You have activated two secret doors. On either side of you, the walls slide up to the ceiling to reveal two more ancient droids. Their electronic eyes glow red, and they step forward.

There is no way out.

You must combat the two droids to proceed.

Note: If you defeated the droid in the previous chamber, you can use the vibro-ax to cut off the heads of these two droids. By cutting off their heads, you will shut down their circuits. If you do not have the vibro-ax, you must choose one of your own weapons to disable the arms of these two droids. Each droid has three arms.

To disable the arms of both droids: Concentrate on one droid. Add your weaponry# to your weapon's close-range# +1 for your confront#. Roll the 12-dice to disable the first arm of this droid.

If your confront# is equal to or more than your roll#, you may proceed to disable the droid's second arm.

If your confront# is lower than your roll#, subtract the difference from your MP total and repeat this confront, doubling your confront# for your new confront#. Repeat this confront with the new confront# until you have defeated the droids.

Once you have disabled all three of the droid's arms, you must follow the same procedure to combat the second droid. When you defeat each droid, they fall to the floor, drained of energy.

To cut off the droids' heads: Add your strength# to your stealth# +2 for your confront#. Roll the 12-dice to cut off the head of the first droid.

> *If your confront# is equal to or more than your roll#,* add the difference to your MP total and proceed to combat the second droid using the same equation.

> *If your confront# is lower than your roll#,* subtract the difference from your MP total. Now add +4 to your confront# for your new confront#. Roll the 12-dice again to continue to combat the first droid. Repeat this confront with the new confront# until you have defeated both droids.

After you have defeated both droids, add 10MP to your MP total (30MP for Advanced Level players).

Both droids have been defeated. The humming sound in the air stops, and the round table separates in half. You walk around the table and see that it has parted to reveal a hidden stairway. The stairway leads even deeper into the ancient tower.

You go down the stairs. It is dark, and you try to turn your infrared goggles back on. Their battery is dead. You put the stormtrooper helmet back on. It's uncomfortable, but at least the helmet's infrared lenses help you see.

At the bottom of the stairs, you reach a tunnel entrance. You walk through.

Your boots make squishing sounds on the tunnel floor. It is covered with water, and you feel as if you are walking through a very long puddle. As you move forward, the water becomes deeper. Soon, it is above your knees.

By the time you emerge from the tunnel, the water is up to your waist. You enter a large cave. High above you, stalactites dangle from the cave ceiling. You look around, trying to find a ledge so you can climb out of the cold water.

Your leg brushes against an object, and you think it might be a rock. But when you try to find it with your boot, it is no longer there.

Nearby, you see bubbles rise to the surface of the water. You realize something is down there. Something *alive*.

The surface of the water explodes as a giant wormlike creature rises out of the water. It opens its mouth to reveal dozens of small, sharp teeth.

Just beyond the creature, you see some rocks. If you can make it that far, you might be able to escape.

You can choose to fight or evade the creature.

To fight: Choose your weapon. Your weaponry# plus your weapon's close-range# −1 is your confront#. Roll the 6-dice to combat the creature.

> If your confront# is equal to or more than your roll#, add the difference +2 to your MP total and proceed.

> If your confront# is lower than your roll#, subtract the difference from your MP total and repeat this confront. Once you have defeated the giant worm you may continue to the rocks.

To evade (without Power): Your stealth# +2 is your confront#. Roll the 12-dice to evade the creature and escape to the nearby rocks.

If your confront# is equal to or *more than your roll#,* add the difference +3 to your MP total and proceed.

If your confront# is lower than your roll#, subtract the difference from your MP total. Now double your confront#, for your new confront#. Roll the 12-dice again to evade the creature.

> *If your new confront# is equal to or more than your roll#,* you may proceed.

> *If your new confront# is lower than your roll#,* subtract 1 from your MP total and repeat this confront with the new confront# until you have made it to the rocks.

To evade (using Power)*: Choose your Evasion Power. Add your stealth# and Jedi# to your Power's low-resist# for your confront#. Roll the 6-dice to evade the creature and escape to the nearby rocks.

If your confront# is equal to or more than your roll#, add the difference to your MP total and proceed.

If your confront# is lower than your roll#, subtract the difference from your MP total and repeat this confront until you have evaded the creature.

*Note: This counts as one of the two Power uses you are allowed in this Mission.

You climb onto the rocks. They form a natural bridge to the far end of the cave. You run across the bridge and arrive at a metal doorway.

The doorway is built into the wall of the cave. You enter the doorway and find yourself standing in some kind of turbolift.

A single button glows dimly in the turbolift. It may be the way out, but it could also be another trap. You have no idea what awaits you, but you know too well that your mission isn't over. So many people are counting on you, and there's so little time.

You press the button and the turbolift rises slowly. It doesn't have a door — you must be careful not to fall.

The turbolift stops, and you step into a large chamber. You have seen chambers like this before, but only in books. You are inside a giant computer system. It must be thousands of years old.

At the far end of the room a small metal ball hangs in the air. The ball is shiny, and has three glowing red photoreceptors. These are its eyes. The ball is an antique droid. It floats toward you. You ready your weapon.

"Please do not fire," the metal ball says. "I am Q-7N, left here by the builders of this fortress."

You look into one of its eyes. "What is your function?" you ask.

"I am in charge of the security of this fortress. I have guarded it for centuries," the droid replies. "Please allow me to scan you." One of its eyes glows, projecting a beam of light onto you.

"Why are you scanning me?" you ask.

"You must be very brave and clever to have come this far," says the droid, not answering your question. It floats backward and you step forward, trying not to let it out of your sight.

"Tell me how to get out of here," you say. "I have friends on the outside who need my help!"

"Friends?" Q-7N dips slightly in the air. "More invaders like yourself? I'm afraid I can't allow that." Two of the droid's eyes glow green.

"But I'm not an invader!" you protest.

"We shall see," replies the droid. Suddenly, the floor opens up beneath you.

You fall helplessly through a trapdoor!

You land with a thud upon a huge pile of glittering treasures. Prized jewels and ornamental weapons are spread throughout the room. You slide down the pile until you reach the stone floor.

There's a tall entryway in the treasure chamber, and you walk toward it. You are about to open it when you hear blaster fire on the other side. You step back into the center of the room. You don't know what's about to come through that door, but you make yourself ready.

The door shatters into a million pieces, and two stormtroopers run into the room. "Look!" yells one. "Treasure!"

At the sight of stormtroopers, you realize you must fight them one at a time or all at once.

One at a time: Choose your weapon. Add your weaponry# to your weapon's mid-range# for your confront#. Roll the 6-dice to combat the first stormtrooper.

If your confront# is equal to or more than your roll#, add the difference to your MP total and proceed to combat the second stormtrooper using the same confront equation.

If your confront# is lower than your roll#, subtract the difference from your MP total. Repeat this confront until you have defeated both stormtroopers.

Both at once: Add your weaponry# to your weapon's mid-range# +1 for your confront#. Roll the 12-dice to fight both stormtroopers.

If your confront# is equal to or more than your roll#, add 7MP to your MP total, and proceed to combat the stormtroopers.

If your confront# is lower than your roll#, subtract the difference from your MP total. Now double your confront# for your new confront#. Roll the 12-dice again to combat the stormtroopers.

If your new confront# is equal to or more than your roll#, you may proceed.

If your new confront# is lower than your roll#, subtract the difference from your MP total. Repeat this confront with the new confront# until you have defeated both stormtroopers.

If you are an Advanced Level player, add 25MP to your MP total.

The two stormtroopers lie on the floor. You thought that you had gotten both of them, but one trooper shifts.

"Why . . . ?" gasps the fallen stormtrooper. "Why did you shoot us? We could have shared the treasure! You . . . you're one of us!"

You forgot you were wearing stormtrooper armor. "I'm not a thief!" you yell at the trooper. You remove your helmet and throw it aside. "And I'm certainly not one of you!"

"Really?" says the stormtrooper. "Well, that changes everything!" His voice sounds familiar, and you try to remember who it sounds like. Suddenly, both stormtroopers seem to flicker slightly. A second later, they vanish into thin air.

"They were holograms?!" you yell. "I wasted ammo on stormtrooper *holograms*?!"

"I'm afraid you did," says the droid as it enters the shattered doorway.

You stare at Q-7N. "That was *your* voice I heard from the stormtrooper."

"Correct," the floating droid replies. "When I scanned you, I replicated your image and generated the holograms. I needed to see how you would behave if other creatures, like you, tried to enter into this tower."

"Well, I'm glad I passed your test," you say. "But you'd better believe if any real stormtroopers made it into your fortress, they'd do worse than raid the place! Now . . . will you please help me get out of here? I have to communicate with my friends!"

"On one condition: You will take me with you," says Q-7N.

"What?!" you ask, truly surprised.

"I am curious," says the droid. "I wish to study your people." The droid rotates and looks around the room. "Besides, after so many thousands of years, I think I need a vacation."

"It's a deal," you say. "Lead the way, Q-7N."

Q-7N leads you to another turbolift. You rise to a higher level, then follow the droid down a dark hallway. It ends suddenly at a large stone doorway.

"This will get us outside," explains the small, floating droid.

"Stay close to me then," you advise. "There are stormtroopers outside, and they *aren't* holograms!"

The large stone door slides into the wall and you step outside. You are on the ground level, and the droid is suspended at your side.

"You there!" calls a nearby voice. You turn quickly and bring your gun up. But the stormtrooper's blaster rifle is pointed at the ground. "What are you doing out of uniform?"

The floating droid whispers to you, "Maybe you shouldn't have thrown away your helmet."

If you shoot at this stormtrooper, the sound of blaster fire may bring more troopers. You can choose to talk your way out of this one, use Power, or fight the trooper.

To talk your way out: Your charm# +1 is your confront#. Roll the 6-dice to make a good excuse for what happened to your helmet.

If your confront# is equal to or more than your roll#, the stormtrooper gives you a new helmet. Add 7MP to your MP total.

If your confront# is lower than your roll#, the stormtrooper does not believe your excuse, and you'll have to fight.

To use Power*: Choose your Evasion Power. Add your charm# and Jedi# to your Power's low-resist# for your confront#. Roll the 6-dice to evade the stormtrooper.

If your confront# is equal to or more than your roll#, add the difference to your MP total and proceed.

If your confront# is lower than your roll#, subtract the difference from your MP total. The stormtrooper does not believe your excuse, and you'll have to fight.

*Note: This counts as one of two Power uses you are allowed in this Mission.

To fight: Choose your weapon. Add your weaponry# to your weapon's close-range# for your confront#. Roll the 12-dice to combat the stormtrooper.

If your confront# is equal to or more than your roll#, add the difference to your MP total and proceed.

If your confront# is lower than your roll#, subtract the difference from your MP total. Now double your confront# for your new confront#. Roll the 12-dice again to combat the stormtrooper.

If your new confront# is equal to or more than your roll#, add the difference −1 to your MP total and proceed.

If your new confront# is lower than your roll#, subtract I from your MP total and repeat this confront with the new confront# until you have defeated the stormtrooper. After you have defeated this stormtrooper, remove his helmet and put it on your own head.

If you talked your way out or used Power, add 10MP to your MP total (25MP for Advanced Level players). If you fought, add 7MP to your MP total (15MP for Advanced Level players).

"This helmet stinks," you mumble.

"Then I'm glad I do not have the ability to smell," says Q-7N.

You adjust your comlink to the proper frequency and whisper: "General Dodonna? Do you read me?"

"You're alive!" says Dodonna. "We feared you'd been captured . . . or worse!"

"I'm on the inside of the crash site," you report, "and I'm disguised as a stormtrooper."

"We don't want to accidentally shoot you," says Dodonna. "How can we recognize you?"

"I'll be the only stormtrooper who drops his weapons and surrenders! But first, I'm going to see what kind of damage I can do on the inside." You switch off the comlink and turn to Q-7N.

"The outside world is so large!" says the floating droid.

"If you want to live to see more of it," you suggest, "you might want to hide here for a while. Things might get pretty rough. . . . "

"Actually," says Q-7N, "I may be able to help. A battle droid is hidden within a nearby stone wall. If we can reach the wall, I can activate the battle droid and order it to attack these stormtroopers."

It sounds like a good plan. Q-7N gives you directions, then stays close to your side as you walk to the stone wall.

Six stormtroopers stand by the wall. It is located beneath a tree that has large, heavy branches. The troopers have their blaster rifles ready, waiting for the Rebel assault. They ignore you, thinking you're just another stormtrooper. Then you spot the stone-faced Imperial captain, standing near the troopers. Inside your helmet, you can hear the sound of your racing heartbeat.

Q-7N floats against the wall and makes a beeping noise. The wall slides away to reveal an ancient, three-armed battle droid. You wait for it to move, but the battle droid remains motionless.

"Something's wrong with it," whispers Q-7N. "There's a manual switch to the left of the battle droid. You'll have to activate it yourself!"

You groan and move forward. Since you don't want to attract attention, you'll have to be careful and quiet. But reaching into the droid's chamber is dangerous! You can either attempt to work the droid's power switch, or knock the droid into shape.

To switch on the droid: Your skill# +2 is your confront#. Roll the 6-dice.

If your confront# is equal to or more than your roll#, add the difference to your MP total and proceed.

If your confront# is lower than your roll#, subtract the difference from your MP total. This switch has not worked. You must now try to knock the battle droid into shape (below).

To knock the droid into shape: Your strength# +1 is your confront#. Roll the 6-dice.

If your confront# is equal to or more than your roll#, add the difference to your MP total and proceed.

If your confront# is lower than your roll#, subtract the difference from your MP total. Add +1 to your confront# for your new confront# and repeat this confront until the droid has been activated.

The battle droid's electronic eyes glow to life. *BZZZT*! It emits a loud noise as it is activated. The stormtroopers and the captain are surprised, and turn toward the fearsome droid. "Attack!" Q-7N commands. He aims an eye in your direction and adds, "but don't harm *this* one."

The battle droid takes one step forward, and the frightened stormtroopers back up.

But a moment later the droid falls to the ground with a crash. Over the past several centuries, it has become a useless, rusted heap.

"Perhaps this wasn't the best plan after all!" Q-7N admits.

The Imperial captain looks at you and his face explodes with rage. "It's the Rebel spy! Get him!"

You can choose to evade or fight the stormtroopers. If you choose to fight, you can take on the stormtroopers all at once or one at a time. You must make your choice now, before reading on.

To evade (without Power): Add your stealth# to your skill# for your confront#. Roll the 6-dice to leap over the stone wall and escape these stormtroopers.

If your confront# is equal to or more than your roll#, add 5MP to your MP total and proceed.

If your confront# is lower than your roll#, subtract the difference from your MP total; you have failed to escape the troopers, and now you must fight.

To evade (using Power)*: Choose your Evasion Power. Add your stealth# and Jedi# to your Power's mid-resist# for your confront#. Roll the 6-dice to leap over the stone wall and escape the stormtroopers.

If your confront# is equal to or more than your roll#, add the difference to your MP total and proceed.

If your confront# is lower than your roll#, subtract the difference from your MP total; you have failed to escape the troopers, and now you must fight.

*Note: This counts as one of two Power uses you are allowed in this Mission. If you have already used Power twice, you cannot use Power here.

To fight all at once: Choose your weapon. Add your weaponry# to your weapon's mid-range# +3 for your confront#. Roll the 12-dice to fire a blast at a tree branch that hangs above the six stormtroopers.

> *If your confront# is equal to or more than your roll#*, the branch falls upon all six troopers. Award yourself 10MP and leap over the wall.

> *If your confront# is lower than your roll#*, subtract the difference from your MP total; you must now combat the stormtroopers one at a time.

To fight one at a time: Choose your weapon. Add your weaponry# to your weapon's mid-range# for your confront#. Roll the 6-dice to combat the first stormtrooper.

> *If your confront# is equal to or more than your roll#*, add the difference to your MP total and proceed to combat the second stormtrooper, using the same confront equation.

> *If your confront# is lower than your roll#*, subtract the difference from your MP total. Repeat this confront until you have neutralized all six stormtroopers. When you reach the fifth trooper, add +1 to your confront#. After that, you may leap over the wall.

After you leap over the stone wall, add 10MP to your MP total (30MP for Advanced Level players).

Blaster bolts tear at the ground near your running feet as you race from the stone wall. The Imperial captain is shooting at you. You keep running, dodging the blaster bolts, and looking for the tree where you hid your speeder bike.

"Wait for me!" says Q-7N, who speeds through the air, trying to keep up. "Sorry about that battle droid . . . I had no idea it was all rusted!"

"Forget it," you say, racing around an outside corner of the stone tower. As you round the corner, you come face-to-face with two stormtroopers setting up a portable laser cannon. Q-7N whips around and comes to a stop near your helmet.

"What have you got there?" asks one of the stormtroopers, looking at Q-7N. "Some new kind of droid?"

You could fight your way out of this situation, but you're running low on ammunition, and you'd have to fight the troopers one at a time. It might be best if you talk your way out of this one, and save your ammo for later. Choose a bluff, use Power, or fight.

To bluff: Your charm# +1 is your confront#. Roll the 6-dice to bluff your way past the two stormtroopers.

If your confront# is equal to or more than your roll#, add the difference to your MP total and proceed.

If your confront# is lower than your roll#, subtract the difference from your MP total. The stormtroopers know you're lying. You'll have to fight them.

To use Power*: Choose your Evasion Power. Add your charm# and Jedi# to your Power's low-resist# for your confront#. Roll the 6-dice to evade the stormtroopers.

If your confront# is equal to or more than your roll#, add the difference to your MP total and proceed.

If your confront# is lower than your roll#, subtract the difference from your MP total. The stormtroopers know you're lying. You'll have to fight.

*Note: This counts as one of the two Power uses you are allowed in this Mission. If you have already used Power twice, you cannot use Power here.

To fight: Add your weaponry# to your weapon's high-range# +2 for your confront#. Roll the 12-dice to combat the first stormtrooper.

If your confront# is equal to or more than your roll#, add the difference to your MP total and proceed to combat the second trooper, using the same confront equation.

If your confront# is lower than your roll#, subtract the difference from your MP total. Now double your confront# for your new confront#. Roll the 12-dice again to combat the trooper.

If your new confront# is equal to or more than your roll#, proceed to combat the second trooper.

If your new confront# is lower than your roll#, subtract the difference from your MP total. Repeat this confront with the new confront# until you have defeated both troopers.

After you have escaped, add 20MP to your MP total (35MP for Advanced Level players).

Q-7N flies beside you as you run into the jungle, away from the ancient tower.

"I don't think I could've done anymore back there," you say, "short of getting myself neutralized."

"You fight with great skill," says Q-7N.

"If I can reach my friends, I can describe the layout of the crash site and tell them how to attack."

The speeder bike is exactly where you left it at the base of the giant tree. You climb onto the bike, and the small droid sets itself down over the navicomputer.

Just as you start the engine, a laser blast glances off you and explodes against the tree. You are not hurt, but your second comlink is destroyed. You look behind you just in time to see two Imperial speeder bikes heading toward you. Each of the speeder bikes carries a scout trooper, and one of them just fired at you. Behind the scout trooper is a military landspeeder filled with stormtroopers. It flies into view and you see that one of its passengers is the Imperial captain.

You hit the throttle and your speeder bike thrusts forward. You keep your head down and hang onto the handlebars.

"Oh, no!" you yell over the roar of the engine.

"What is it now?" asks Q-7N as you swoop under some low branches.

"It's this stormtrooper helmet I'm wearing!" you yell. "If I take it off, I won't be able to see in the darkness! But if I leave it on, the Rebels might think *I'm* a stormtrooper . . . and shoot me!"

Just then, one of the scout troopers speeds up alongside you. The other scout trooper is directly behind you.

You can choose to evade, to outrun, or to fight. To fight, you must take on the scout troopers one at a time.

To evade: Add your stealth# to your speeder's stealth# +1 for your confront#. Roll the 6-dice to make a daring escape through a fallen, hollow tree.

If your confront# is equal to or more than your roll#, add the difference to your MP total. You have lost the scout troopers and may proceed.

If your confront# is lower than your roll#, subtract the difference from your MP total. You have failed to evade the scout troopers and must now fight (next page).

To outrun the scout troopers: Add your speeder's speed# to your skill# for your confront#. Roll the 6-dice to accelerate through the jungle.

If your confront# is equal to or more than your roll#, add the difference to your MP total. You have left the scout troopers far behind and may proceed.

If your confront# is lower than your roll#, subtract the difference from your MP total. You have failed to outrun the scout troopers and must now fight (next page).

To fight the scout troopers behind you: Add your stealth# to your skill# for your confront#. Roll the 6-dice to hit your brakes and let the back of your speeder bike knock the rear scout trooper off his bike.

> *If your confront# is equal to or more than your roll#*, add the difference to your MP total and proceed to combat the other scout trooper (below).

> *If your confront# is lower than your roll#*, subtract the difference from your MP total and repeat this confront until you have defeated this trooper. Then combat the other scout trooper (below).

To fight the scout trooper beside you: Add your weaponry# to your speeder's weaponry# +1 for your confront#. Roll the 6-dice to blast the trooper's bike and cause him to crash.

> *If your confront# is equal to or more than your roll#*, add the difference to your MP total and proceed.

> *If your confront# is lower than your roll#,* subtract the difference from your MP total. Repeat this confront until you have defeated the trooper.

After you have dealt with these two scout troopers (either by fighting or evading), add 20 to your MP total (45 for Advanced Level players).

"That was a close call!" you observe. Q-7N agrees. In front of you, you can see a clearing in the jungle. "Hey, that's where I discovered a set of ruins!" You race for the clearing, hoping that you'll still reach your friends in time. The captain is still alive, and it looks like you might need their help in capturing him.

As you arrive at the clearing, you slow your speeder bike and pull up next to a tall stone pillar. You look around, but don't see any signs of movement. "I thought my friends would have reached this place by now," you say.

The sound of blaster fire echoes around you. Large clumps of dirt and stone fly into the air as each blast connects with the ground. You're knocked off your bike and Q-7N sails off into the sky, landing beyond some distant trees.

Shaking your head, you look up and see the Imperial military landspeeder. The stone-faced captain is laughing at you. You reach for your weapon, but it has fallen out of reach.

"Thought you could escape us, did you?" gloats the captain. He aims his laser pistol at your head.

The sound of speeding metal fills the air as Q-7N rockets out from behind the trees. Flying at an incredibly high speed, he zooms toward the captain.

The ball-like droid hits hard against the captain's hand, knocking the laser pistol from his grip. The captain yelps with pain, and one of the stormtroopers shoots Q-7N. One shot appears to connect with the small droid, and Q-7N shrieks and falls to the ground. You take advantage of the panic above you, and locate your weapon.

With one shot you can disable the landspeeder.

To disable the landspeeder: Add your weaponry# to your weapon's far-range# for your confront#. Roll the 6-dice to shoot at the main thruster on the landspeeder.

If your confront# is equal to or more than your roll#, add the difference to your MP total and proceed.

If your confront# is lower than your roll#, subtract the difference from your MP total. Now double your confront# for your new confront#. Roll the 12-dice to shoot the thruster.

> *If your new confront# is equal to or more than your roll#,* add the difference minus 1 to your MP total and proceed.

> *If your new confront# is lower than your roll#,* subtract 1 from your MP total and repeat this confront with the new confront# until you have disabled the landspeeder.

The landspeeder spins out of control and crashes into a high stone wall at the edge of the clearing.

"Q-7N!" you yell. "Are you okay?!" The ball-like droid is lying on some blaster-scarred gravel. It's sensors are no longer lit.

Your attention returns to the wrecked landspeeder. The captain appears to be unconscious, but five stormtroopers spill out of the sides of the vehicle. They hit the stone wall hard. The wall does not appear to be steady. A clear shot to the right stone could cause the wall to topple.

One of the troopers yells, "Get that Rebel!"

You can choose to fight the troopers all at once (by shooting down the wall) or one at a time.

All at once: Choose your weapon. Your weaponry# plus your weapon's far-range# is your confront#. Roll the 6-dice to shoot the stone that will bring the wall down.

If your confront# is equal to or more than your roll#, add the difference to your MP total and proceed.

If your confront# is lower than your roll#, subtract the difference from your MP total. The stormtroopers have run away from the wall, and you will have to combat them one at a time.

One at a time: Choose your weapon. Your weaponry# plus your weapon's far-range# is your confront#. Roll the 6-dice to combat the first stormtrooper.

If your confront# is equal to or more than your roll#, add the difference to your MP total and proceed to combat the second trooper.

If your confront# is lower than your roll#, subtract the difference from your MP total. Repeat this confront until you have defeated all five stormtroopers.

After you have defeated the stormtroopers, add 15MP to your MP total (25MP for Advanced Level players).

Neutralized stormtroopers lie everywhere, and the air smells like blaster fire. You run over to Q-7N, who lies broken on the ground. One photoreceptor looks as though it has been torn from the ancient droid.

"Halt, trooper!" a voice yells behind you. You know the voice, and you raise your hands into the air.

"Don't shoot!" you say as you drop your weapon and raise your arms over your head. "It's me, General Dodonna!"

"Hold your fire!" General Dodonna shouts to the Rebel troops behind him. You take the stormtrooper helmet off and drop it to the ground. A smile crosses your face as you ask, "What took you so long, General?"

"We ran into some stormtrooper trouble of our own," replies Dodonna. He glances around at the wreckage. "It looks like you've had quite a day."

Pointing at the crashed military landspeeder, you say, "The Imperial captain is over there. Last I looked, he was knocked out. But he may be able to tell us what his mission was all about."

"Good job, soldier," says Dodonna.

"One other thing," you say. "I met an old droid, and it wound up saving my life. If we can fix it, I think it would be a great help to the Rebel Alliance."

"We'll see what we can do," says Dodonna. "The Alliance can always use a new friend!"

Your mission has been successfully completed. The stormtroopers were defeated before they could relay your position to the Empire. The Imperial captain has been captured alive and can be questioned about the purpose of his mission to the Yavin system.

Reward yourself with 250 MP.

THE
AFTER-
MISSION

Q-7N's various pieces were spread across a cold metal worktable in the Rebel base's repair shop. Artoo examined the broken bits of ancient gears and circuits, then turned to Threepio and let out a series of beeps.

"No, Artoo," said Threepio. "I haven't seen such an old droid in my entire life. At least not outside of my studies. Do you really think you can repair the little fellow?"

Artoo responded with a series of whistling beeps, then rotated his domed head to examine an especially damaged piece of Q-7N. One of Artoo's front panels opened and he extended a maintenance appendage.

"Oh, dear," said Threepio. "You're going to use your laser welder? I can't bear to watch! Excuse me, Artoo, but I think now's a good time for me to go find Master Luke!" Threepio tottered out of the repair shop.

When Captain Skeezer awoke, he was lying on a metal-framed cot in a cold room. The room was a medical unit at the Rebel base on Yavin Four. His wrists and ankles were secured to the cot, and he knew he wasn't strong enough to escape.

A man dressed as a doctor entered the room. He wore a mask over his mouth and nose. Captain Skeezer looked up. "Are you with the Rebellion?" he asked.

"Yup," said the man. "But I'm a doctor, so it's nothing personal. I'll cure anybody."

"What's your name?" sneered Skeezer.

"Solo," said the masked man. "Doctor Han Solo."

"I suppose you expect me to talk, Doctor Solo," said Skeezer.

"Not really," said Solo. "You are in bad shape, pal. I'm surprised you're talking at all!"

Skeezer looked concerned. "Bad shape?"

"Yeah, you got pretty busted up out there. You're just lucky we've got a good supply of bacta to take care of you." Solo pulled a lever, and a large drum of bacta lowered from the ceiling. "You'll be better in no time, even though you'll wind up in a prison camp."

Skeezer took a deep breath. "I don't *feel* like I'm in bad shape," he said.

"Believe me," said Solo, "we really need to get you into this bacta tank. The bacta will heal you just fine. And don't worry about the bacta. It's Imperial quality! We got it from the Death Star before we blew it up."

"You what?!" Skeezer exclaimed.

"Yeah," said Solo, smiling behind his mask. "Hard to believe, isn't it? That us Rebels blew up the big, bad Death Star?"

"No!" yelled Skeezer, who was starting to sweat. "I mean . . . I realized the Death Star had been destroyed, but . . . you say this bacta came from there?!"

"That's right!" said Solo. "Good thing we got it, or else you'd never heal from the wounds you've suffered!"

"But I feel fine! I don't need any bacta!" Skeezer's voice had risen to a scream.

"Hey," said the masked man as he wagged a finger at the captain. "Last time I looked, *I'm* the doctor around here!"

"No! I beg you!" shrieked Skeezer. "That bacta isn't any good! It's contaminated!"

"Contaminated? Really?" The doctor sounded concerned. "Gee, that changes everything. I'll have to let my assistant operate on you." The doctor pushed a button and a door slid open.

Captain Skeezer looked up and saw a giant Wookiee in the opened doorway.

"The patient is all yours, Doctor Chewbacca," said Solo. Chewbacca growled once. Captain Skeezer fainted.

Han Solo removed the mask from his face, and then left the room with Chewbacca. In the hallway, they met with Luke and Leia, just as See-Threepio came clanking around the corner.

"How's our Imperial prisoner doing?" Leia asked. "You didn't scare him to death, did you?"

"No, he's healthy as a well-fed gundark," said Han. "But he sure got plenty scared when he thought we were going to use bacta from the Death Star on him."

"I don't understand," said Threepio. "I thought the bacta on the Death Star was destroyed!"

"The bacta *was* destroyed, Threepio," explained Luke, "but the Imperial captain didn't know it. Han *tricked* him so we could learn more about the bacta!"

"You got that right, kid," said Solo. "According to the captain, that bacta was contaminated!"

"Contaminated?!" Luke exclaimed. "First we were wondering why the Death Star was carrying so much bacta, and now . . . now it turns out the bacta wasn't even any good?!"

"Well," Han mused, "whatever the Empire had in mind for that bacta, those plans probably ended when the Death Star exploded. But when the captain wakes up, I've got some questions about *his* mission to the Yavin system — "

"Oh, no!" interrupted Leia. "I . . . I could be wrong . . . but I think I know what the Empire was doing with that bacta!" Leia stepped closer to Luke and Solo and tried to keep the fear out of her voice. "We have to meet with General Dodonna immediately!"

NEXT MISSION: ESCAPE FROM THYFERRA!